Food WISE

Healthy Eating for
Primary Schools

By Primrose Appleby
and Jan Tilley

TITLE

Series Name: **Foodwise** - *Introducing Food Technology and Healthy Eating in primary schools*
Book Number: K2232
ISBN Number: ISBN 1-843210-28-2
Published: 2002

AUTHORS

Primrose Appleby and Jan Tilley

ACKNOWLEDGEMENTS

KCP Publications wishes to acknowledge the work of the following people in the various stages of publishing this resource.

Designer: Michelle Peacock
Illustrator: Geraldine Sloane
Publisher: Pauline Scanlan

PUBLISHERS

KCP Publications Ltd,

P.O. Box 293

Hemel Hempstead

HP2 7WD

Phone: +44 (0)7050-607-359

Fax: +44 (0)7020-954-582

Email: admin@kcppublications.com

COPYING NOTICE

COPYRIGHT

KCP Publication specialises in publishing educational resources for teachers and students across a wide range of curriculum areas, at both primary and secondary levels. If you wish to know more about our resources, or if you think your resource ideas have publishing potential, please contact us at one of the above addresses.

Contents

UNIT ONE - Safe Food

UNIT TWO - Smart Choices

UNIT THREE - Bread - The Ultimate Snack

UNIT FOUR - Healthy Vegetables

UNIT FIVE - Milk

UNIT SIX - Don't get browned off!

Teaching Food Technology

Points to consider:

- **Understand** that the specific objectives of teaching primary school students about food is to lay firm and accurate foundations so that they can make judgements and choices backed by accurate knowledge.

- **Teach** students that food-related learning not only concerns what takes place in the classroom, but also food practices throughout the school.

- **Acknowledge** that working with food in the classroom requires a positive approach. Avoid using the terms 'good' and 'bad' foods. It is important to encourage a wide variety of food in the practical activities, supporting current food and nutrition guidelines. Copies of the guidelines are readily available from health educators.

- **Choose** topics that are relevant to students' everyday lives and which hold their interest and extend their skills. Be prepared to choose topical issues as a basis for investigations. For example, reports that children do not eat enough vegetables or discussing appropriate food for a school camp.

- **Provide** quality learning experiences which help develop fine motor skills in a progressive way, eg. chopping and slicing different foods.

- **Explain** clearly to your students the importance of nutrition to their health and wellbeing.

- **Recognise** that we are all bombarded with information about food, much of it conflicting. Students need the skills to analyse what they are being told and put it into a personal context.

- **Encourage** students to transfer knowledge and skills between subject areas, for example, using Maths when calculating ingredients or costing. Social skills can also be enhanced when sharing food.

- **Be conscious** of religious and cultural sensitivities when planning. Include in your programme topics and activities that have a cultural focus. Perhaps design units which feature the cuisine of a particular country relevant to the class.

Teaching Food Technology

- **Be aware** and prepared for health and safety issues which could arise from the work you undertake, especially in relation to visits.

- **Encourage** students to eat five portions of fruit and vegetables each day, wholegrain bread, cereals and milk. Food chosen for practical classroom work should be low in fat and sugar content. Low fat methods of cooking include baking, grilling, steaming , and microwaving. The recommended food requirements for good nutrition can be investigated and applied.

- **Choose** foods that are easily obtainable and affordable, yet interesting.

- **Introduce** the use of new foods and new combinations of foods.

- **Devise** ways of encouraging students to taste and record their reactions.

Students need to know which foods to eat more of and which to eat in small amounts. Nutrients and their functions are difficult to understand and should be introduced at a later date. Food needs to be looked at as a whole with a focus on variety.

Five Plus a Day

The 'Five Plus a Day' campaign encourages people to have five portions of fruit and vegetables a day. A 'portion' is as much as can be held in a cupped hand.

This campaign can form a basis for a unit of work.

5 DAY

5 + a DAY

Managing Food Technology in a General Classroom

B. ESTABLISHING A FOOD TECHNOLOGY AREA IN AN EXISTING CLASSROOM

In the absence of a purpose-built area each school will need to decide where food work will be done. Once the food area is designated special precautions must be taken to ensure safety and hygiene at all times. Equipment for foods work should be kept for just that purpose.

▶ Points to consider when using an existing classroom:

1. Running hot and cold water are essential to help ensure a clean environment for food preparation and hand washing.

2. Tables should be covered with a plastic cloth to give a hygienic working surface or resurfaced with a laminated material. Tables should be cleaned with a hygiene spray before use.

3. A mobile unit with a microwave oven or bench top hot plate/ oven, together with cooking utensils and equipment can be shared by several rooms.

4. Unless food is to be used on the day of purchase a refrigerator is vital.

5. If food is to be stored long term suitable cupboard space will also be required.

6. Safety aspects of fire and electrical equipment and storage of knives need to be addressed.

7. Display and resource areas are important to provide students with access to ideas and information.

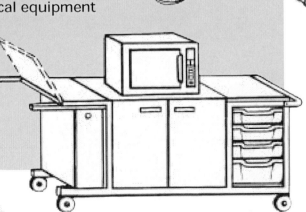

Equipping an Area for Foods Work

In addition to ensuring that equipment for food preparation is kept solely for that purpose, also check that any donated or second hand equipment is free from cracks or chips and thoroughly cleaned.

Equipment will be required as follows:

1. **Food preparation**
   - Unbreakable bowls and measuring jugs (metric!) and a good selection of utensils and cutlery are essential. These could be on a portable food preparation trolley (see illustration on page 6) if they are to be shared by several classes.

   - Chopping boards should be easy to clean. If plastic, soak in bleach regularly. Laminated boards are difficult to keep clean and are unhygienic.

   - Knives need to be selected with size of hands in mind.

2. **Food storage**
   - Keep food storage to a minimum. Have students bring large coffee jars and ice cream containers with fitted lids to use for dry ingredients. These should be clearly labelled and dated.

3. **Cooking equipment**
   - Purchase saucepans, oven trays which fit the oven. Use plastic/ glass for the microwave.

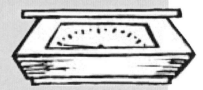

4. **Measuring equipment**
   - Use metric measuring spoons, cups and scales.

5. **Electrical equipment**
   - Over time collect a jug or kettle, toaster, electric frypan, toasted sandwich maker, hand mixer, microwave, small bench oven, hot plate, multi-point power box and food processor, if possible.

6. **Food service**
   - Have available plates, cutlery, tablecloths or placemats.

Kitchen Hygiene and Safety

Attention to aspects of hygiene and safety is crucial to avoid food poisoning and possible cross infection.

> **These aspects include:**
>
> 1. hand washing facilities, hand or paper towels, soap and bowl;
>
> 2. dish washing facilities, disposable cloths, detergent, pot cleaners and brushes, disinfectant and bleach (stored away from food);
>
> 3. heat proof oven gloves and mats for hot pots and dishes;
>
> 4. washing facilities for dish cloths, tea towels and hand towels;
>
> 5. protective clothing such as an apron or an old shirt;
>
> 6. a first aid kit and fire extinguisher.

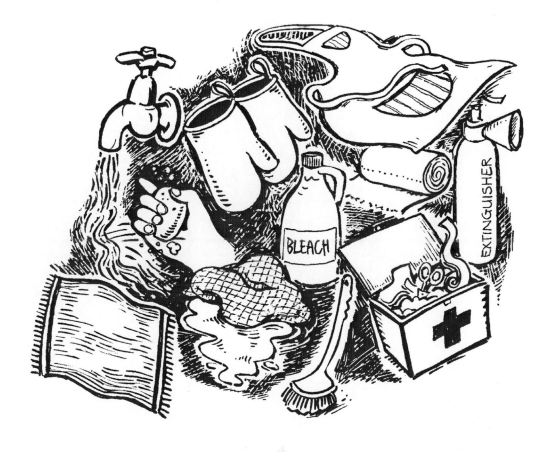

8

Classroom Routines

Establishing classroom routines when working with food help to keep the teacher sane! Routines can make the difference between spending hours cleaning up after practical foods work or not.

These routines can include:

1. knowing where to put schoolbags;

2. keeping floor spaces clean;

3. washing hands;

4. wearing aprons;

5. collecting ingredients;

6. organising equipment;

7. keeping to the designated food area (this can be marked on the floor);

8. washing up;

9. working in rostered groups;

10. wrapping food waste and other rubbish and disposal;

11. leaving the workspace clean and tidy.

The following three pages have been included to assist with establishing these routines. It is recommended that they are enlarged, laminated and displayed on the wall in the Food Technology area.

Preparing Food Safely

SIMPLE RULES

- Wash your hands well with soap and water before starting.

- Make sure your hands are dry when turning electric switches off and on.

- Have a clear floor space. Make sure there is nothing to fall over on the floor. Never run, even when in a hurry.

- Wipe up spills at once.

- Use oven gloves when you move hot dishes and pans.

- Turn pot handles inwards so that you can't knock them over.

- Lift pot lids carefully so that the steam is away from you.

- Never reach across a hot saucepan of food - steam can burn.

- Hold knife blades downwards when moving around the room.

- Know where the First Aid Kit and fire extinguisher are.

- Run cold water on any burns for at least ten minutes.

- Cover any cuts or sores with a plaster or micropore tape.

When You Are Cooking

Before you start:

1. Turn on the oven, if needed.

2. Collect all the equipment you will require.

3. Read any instructions right through and ask if there is something you don't understand.

4. Take out all the ingredients you need for what you intend to make. This way you will remember to add everything.

5. If you have to measure ingredients, measure them accurately, using level metric measures.

11

Cleaning Code For Food Area

1. Wrap food scraps before putting them in the bin.

2. Scrape and stack all dishes.

3. Use hot water with washing up liquid to wash up in.

4. Wash plastic or glass dishes first, rinse off the soap and drain.

5. Wash the dirtiest dishes last.

6. Dry, using a clean tea towel (or paper towels).

7. Put dishes and equipment away neatly.

8. Wipe the bench and clean out the bowl. Hang out the dishcloth to dry.

Informing Parents and Carers

- Planning ahead which includes the practical activities or visits keeps everyone informed and makes for a smooth operation.

- Advance notice is essential to help parents organise shopping for the necessary ingredients for foods work, or to let parents know if a visit outside school is likely.

- Classroom Assistants and Parent helpers can take small groups of students for practical work, research activities, or to assist on visits. They can also help with the organisation and cleaning up associated with practical work. (See below.)

- Form letters can be sent home with the students giving date, purpose, and any other details related to their work in Food Technology. Two useful sample letters are included on the following two pages.

TRAINING STAFF AND PARENT HELPERS

- Trained helpers can be a valuable assistance to teachers in a classroom.

- Helpers need knowledge of food hygiene and an understanding of curriculum requirements. They can then give appropriate guidance and assistance in helping students to progress and become independent.

- A certificate in food hygiene can provide a good basic grounding for those interested and is available through most local authorities or Colleges.

- Teachers need to clarify their expectations with helpers in terms of classroom routines, safety and general management.

Food Technology
Practical Foods

Date: _____ / _____ / _____

We are doing work in the class on:

_____

We are making:

_____

Could you please supply the following items on this day?

_____
_____
_____
_____
_____

- ●
- ●
- ●
- ●
- ●
- ●
- ●

If your child has any special dietary needs please write and let us know.

We need caregivers to help with the lesson. Please let us know if you are available.

Thank you for your help

Food Technology
Practical Foods

Date: _____ / _____ / _____

We are doing work in the class on:

_____

We are making:

_____

Could you please supply the following items on this day?

_____
_____
_____
_____
_____

- ●
- ●
- ●
- ●
- ●
- ●
- ●

If your child has any special dietary needs please write and let us know.

We need caregivers to help with the lesson. Please let us know if you are available.

Thank you for your help

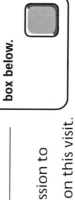

Food Technology
A visit to:

Date of visit: ___ / ___ / ___
Time of visit: _____

As part of our Food Technology unit on: _____

We are visiting: _____

The purpose of this visit is to: _____

Things you need to know about this visit:

● _____
● _____
● _____
● _____
● _____
● _____

If you would like to accompany us on our visit and help supervise please tick the box below.

We would like your permission to take _____ on this visit.

I give/ do not give permission

Please sign here: _____

Food Technology
A visit to:

Date of visit: ___ / ___ / ___
Time of visit: _____

As part of our Food Technology unit on: _____

We are visiting: _____

The purpose of this visit is to: _____

Things you need to know about this visit:

● _____
● _____
● _____
● _____
● _____
● _____

If you would like to accompany us on our visit and help supervise please tick the box below.

We would like your permission to take _____ on this visit.

I give/ do not give permission

Please sign here: _____

Safe Food

PREPARATION

This activity is aimed at increasing students' awareness of the role of food storage in the provision of safe food.

> **Before beginning this activity it would be useful to introduce the topic using these ideas:**
>
> ● discuss times when class members or their families have had food poisoning;
>
> ● role play making a sandwich using all the 'wrong' methods eg: licking fingers, unclean utensils, smelly dish cloth. Ask class members for their reactions at the end;
>
> ● hand out the pre-test sheet, "Safe Food" for students to complete.
>
> ● when students have completed their food handling survey, on page 21, they will need to discuss what is 'unhygienic' about the habits listed.

UNIT 1

Safe Food

Do you know how to store food safely?

Read the sentences below. Tick whether you think each statement is 'sensible' or 'silly'.

	SENSIBLE	SILLY
Put hot foods into a refrigerator	☐	☐
Empty left over canned tomatoes into a container	☐	☐
Store uncovered ham and fresh mince side by side	☐	☐
Allow meat juices to drip in the refrigerator	☐	☐
Clean out the store cupboard regularly.	☐	☐
Leave the fruit bowl on a sunny window ledge	☐	☐
Mix old and new bags of flour together	☐	☐
Store the vegetable rack next to the cooker	☐	☐
Wash the tops of messy bottles	☐	☐
Leave open packets on cupboard shelf	☐	☐
Use foods in rotation from the refrigerator and freezer	☐	☐
Wash all fruit before putting in fruit bowl	☐	☐

Share your answers with a partner then talk about them with your class.

Safe Food

Task

Imagine that another class is doing food studies in their classroom. Your class is going to prepare a resource kit to help make sure they know how to keep the food they use safe to eat. You can present the information in any way you like, such as on a pamphlet, a poster, or a computer presentation. You will need to investigate and gather information to use. Work through the activities in this unit first.

What's perishable?

Do you know what 'perishable' means? Use the information on the following page to set up a class experiment, using everyday foods, find out which foods are most perishable. Also look at the changes over a two week period.

Some foods you could use are shown in the box below.

WARNING:
Do not taste the foods as they could be harmful and may cause food poisoning!

- bacon or salami
- apple
- carrot
- spoon of jam
- slice of bread
- cheese slice
- lettuce
- cornflakes
- milk
- cream cracker
- butter
- chocolate biscuit
- tomato
- potato
- rice
- banana

Safe Food

What's perishable?

1. Place the foods you choose on a moist saucer, covered with cling film, and leave in a warm place in the classroom. Label the saucers with the name of the food.

2. Look every day at your experiment and record changes on a table like the one below.

Food	Day	Changes observed

3. Use the following words, or any others, to describe the changes observed:-

- **nasty smell**
- **slimy appearance**
- **moulds**
- **yeasts**
- **dry**
- **limp**
- **sour**
- **soft**
- **shrivelled**
- **odd colour spots**

4. Which foods were the most perishable? List them.

Safe Food
How should you store?

Show how you know how to store food by writing these foods in the correct storage place shown below. Make your predictions in your book, then compare them with other people.

- chicken
- frozen beans
- ice cream
- bread
- bacon
- ham
- cheese
- minced beef
- cornflakes
- milk
- cream cracker

- cooked left-overs
- sugar
- tea
- cornflakes
- baked beans
- flour
- macaroni
- sultanas
- apple
- chocolate biscuit
- rice

- margarine
- jam
- mayonnaise
- onions
- tomato
- potato
- banana
- lettuce
- carrot
- spoon of jam

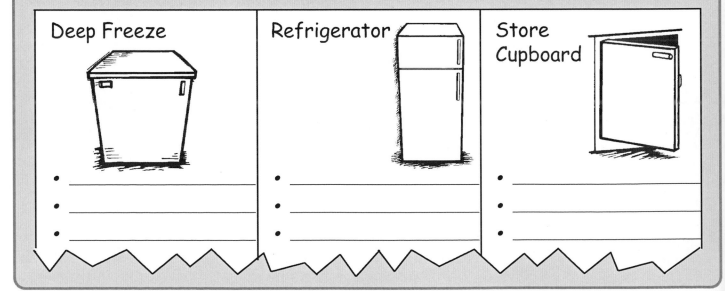

Deep Freeze

Refrigerator

Store Cupboard

UNIT 1

Safe Food
What's the best way to handle food?

Carry out the following survey to find out what your classmates' food handling habits are like. You might also like to try this it on members of your family. Choose ten people and ask them the following questions. Work out in pairs the best way to gather and organise your findings, ready for presentation.

When you are in the kitchen handling food would you:

- **wash** your hands after blowing your nose?

- **let** food cool down before putting it in the refrigerator?

- **never** re-freeze foods which have thawed?

- **cover** foods left out on the bench?

- **wash** your hands after stroking an animal?

- **wash** the can opener after using it?

- **have** a separate cutting board for raw meat?

- **have** a clean tea-towel every day?

- **regularly** bleach or boil the dishcloth?

- **make** sure cuts on hands are covered with clean plasters?

- **always** cover food in the refrigerator?

- **lick** the spoon you are mixing with?

In your book...

1. **Draw a bar chart to show your findings.**

2. **What conclusions can you draw from your survey?**

3. **Write three or four sentences on the food handling habits of the people you surveyed.**

Smart Choices

Task One

Work towards achieving a Healthy Habits Certificate by recording your 'smart choices' for a whole week of eating! Read the information below to put you on the right track!

Smart choices about nutrition and physical fitness can help you develop healthy habits which help you to be the best you can be.

1. Start the day with a good breakfast.

2. Eat a variety of nutritious foods each day.

3. Choose healthy snacks like fruit.

4. Enjoy regular physical activity.

5. Limit inactive times like watching TV or playing video games.

On your checklist...

1. **Whenever you make a 'Smart Choice' about one of the healthy habits listed above, colour in a star on your checklist.**

2. **Count up how many stars you have for each day.**

3. **At the end of the week add up the daily scores to find your totals.**

4. **Put your scores on your Healthy Habits Award Certificate.**

_____'s

Healthy Habits
Checklist

Date from: _____ to _____

▶ **HEALTHY EATING HABITS:**

| | | M. | T. | W. | T. | F. | S. | S. |

1. began the day with a good
energising breakfast

2. refuelled with a variety
of good foods midday
and evening

3. picked healthy snacks like
raw vegetables, fruit,
cheese or yoghurt

My healthy eating scores ☐/3 ☐/3 ☐/3 ☐/3 ☐/3 ☐/3 ☐/3

TOTAL ☐/21

▶ **HEALTHY EXERCISE HABITS:**

| | | M. | T. | W. | T. | F. | S. | S. |

1. did heart healthy activities
like running, skipping,
jumping or biking

2. spent time helping out
around the house or
outside

3. did something active
instead of watching TV

My healthy exercise scores ☐/3 ☐/3 ☐/3 ☐/3 ☐/3 ☐/3 ☐/3

TOTAL ☐/21

UNIT 2

Smart Choices

Task Two

Why do you think it is important for students to have breakfast before they come to school? Do you have breakfast?

In this task your class will be making a 'fast-start' breakfast to get off to an energising start for the day!

The importance of breakfast

Before you make your fast-start breakfast, there is some research for you to undertake.

1. Make a poster which encourages people to have breakfast. Use leaflets available from your local Health Authority and organisations such as the National Heart Foundation and magazine articles to help you.

2. Visit the supermarket and look at the choice of cereals available.

3. Bring in empty cereal packets and compare the nutrition information on the side of the box.

4. Brainstorm in groups and make a class list of all the breakfast foods they have ever had. From this list identify those which could be prepared and served in the classroom.

5. Identify all those foods that could be cooked and/or prepared and served in 15 minutes.

6. Investigate the times foods take to cook and consider personal preferences, for example, toast and eggs.

UNIT 2

Smart Choices

A fast-start breakfast

In groups, investigate and plan a shared fast-start breakfast which is able to be prepared in the classroom.

The final choice must be liked by everyone in the group.

Here are some menu suggestions.

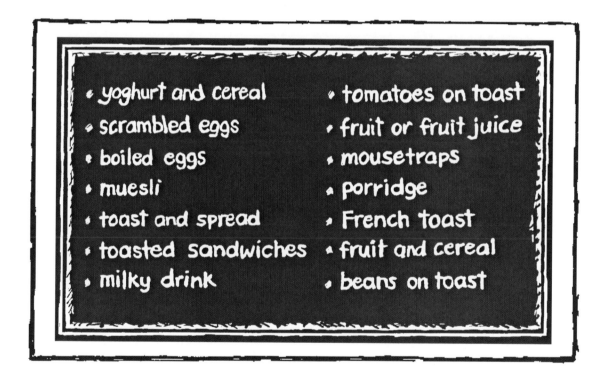

- yoghurt and cereal
- scrambled eggs
- boiled eggs
- muesli
- toast and spread
- toasted sandwiches
- milky drink
- tomatoes on toast
- fruit or fruit juice
- mousetraps
- porridge
- French toast
- fruit and cereal
- beans on toast

When you have decided on your menu you will need to find recipes (if required) and work out how you will get your ingredients. Can you bring some of the ingredients from home?

Smart Choices
A fast-start breakfast

PLANNING YOUR BREAKFAST

- Work in your group and plan who will be bringing which ingredients.

- Prepare a time plan for the breakfast you intend to make - you will be working in groups of four. A time plan is a list of tasks in the order they need to be done.

- The food that takes longest to prepare and cook will need to be prepared first.

- Work out what time you plan to finish and work backwards!

- Opposite is an example. (On this day you were told that you would have breakfast at school.)

TIME PLAN EXAMPLE	
START TIME	(FOR BREAKFAST COOKED AT SCHOOL)
9.00	Wash hands and clean the work surface or cover it with a plastic cloth.
9.00	Collect ingredients
9.05	Person 1: make toast Person 2: cook eggs Person 3: set table Person 4: make the drinks
9.20	Serve the breakfast
9.30	Person 1: stack the dishes Person 2: wash the dishes Person 3: dry the dishes Person 4: tidy up and put away the dishes
9.45	In groups talk about how you breakfast went and score it on the chart

Smart Choices
A fast-start breakfast

Prepare your planned breakfast and then complete the following activities.

> **In your group score your breakfast in the boxes:**
> **5 = high - 1 = low.**
>
> ● Did you finish in the time planned? .... ☐
>
> ● Did you all like the taste of the breakfast? .... ☐
>
> ● How well did your group work together? .... ☐
>
> ● Would you make this breakfast again? .... ☐
>
> **Total** ☐

> **LOOKING FORWARD**
>
> Talk to the class about the breakfast you chose to make, telling them:
>
> ● why you made your choices;
>
> ● which foods were the ones containing carbohydrate, fats and calcium;
>
> ● how long it took to prepare and serve;
>
> ● what changes you could make next time.

> **GET THE BREAKFAST MESSAGE ACROSS**
>
> ● Use your experience to write some jingles or slogans to encourage other people in the school to eat a healthy breakfast every day. Target your message at students and staff. Record them on audio tape.
>
> ● Put up a display in the school library of your Healthy Breakfast posters and have the jingles available at a listening post.
>
> ● You may like to invite your local newspaper to come and see your display and to take a photo for the paper.

UNIT 3

Bread - The Ultimate Snack
What are your favourite bread snacks?

 Now that you have worked out what you mean by 'snack' here is your chance to survey a target market (people between 10-12 years/ people over 20/ girls/ boys) on their preferences for bread snacks. Design a questionnaire for your target market. Look at these guidelines for good questionnaires to help you.

1. Your questions should be clear, brief and focus on favourite bread snacks.

2. Keep to one point per question.

3. Trial your questions on each other to check that the meaning is clear.

4. Avoid leading questions (get your teacher to explain this).

5. Decide whether you want to ask open-ended questions, such as:

   ● *"what is your favourite bread snack like?"*

   ● *"what is it that you like about your favourite bread snack?"*

   or

   closed questions with yes or no answers such as:

   ● *"do you like wholegrain bread?"*

6. Don't make your questionnaire too long.

7. When you have finished your interviews graph or chart the results. You may be able to use a computer for this.

8. Compile a list of the most popular bread snacks.

Bread - The Ultimate Snack
Make and taste some bread snacks

1. Using the information from your questionnaire, research some recipes for the most popular bread snacks, or use the recipes on the previous pages.

2. In groups of two divide up the snack recipes, prepare some of the bread snacks and serve them to another class.

3. With another group have a tasting session and decide which ones you like best.

4. Set up an independent taste panel (grandparents who can come to your class, perhaps!) They will need to use their senses for this.

   They will: - *look at; smell; and taste the bread snacks.*

5. Record the results on a table so that you have clear information to help you decide on a the 'best' bread snacks.

Sample					flavour	texture	colour	smell
1								
2								
3								
4								

6. Use the results to help you decide which bread snacks you will make to share with another class or another community group. You may want to make some changes to improve some of the snacks tasted.

7. Look at advertising techniques used on television, newspapers and magazines to advertise food.

   Identify techniques and words used and apply this information to design your own **healthy bread snack** advertisement. This could be a radio jingle, video sequence of no more than 30 seconds, notice board display.

UNIT 4

5+@DAY

Healthy Vegetables

Do you know...

...that there are at least 300,000 different kinds of plants growing in the world? How many different kinds can you think of?

Many of these are edible (can be eaten) but in fact we eat very few of them. We often stay with those we know, like and can grow ourselves easily.

Another problem is that we tend to be unwilling to try new foods, however, as people travel and experience new things they become more open and willing to experiment with new tastes.

Most of the vegetables we eat nowadays originated in the Near East (Turkey, Lebanon, Syria, Palestine, Israel, Jordan and Iraq) or in the northern regions of South America.

Over time people came to know which foods were safe to eat, readily available, had good texture, flavour and appearance, and stored well. The vegetables we eat today are the descendants of these plants and fulfilled these conditions.

In Europe the climate allows us to grow a wide range of some of the best vegetables in the world. The variations in the soil and climate are suitable for plants from many other parts of the world.

Our world is now facing huge increases in population and shortages in food supply in some areas. We have to find ways of producing good vegetables cheaply and making the best use of our resources.

- Do you like vegetables? In groups discuss why you do or don't like eating your 'greens'!

- To keep healthy you really should eat five or more servings of vegetables daily. How many servings do *you* eat?

- Until very recently families were often self sufficient and grew their own vegetables. Does your family grow any vegetables?

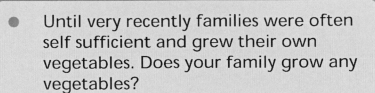

Parts of the plant we eat

When you eat a vegetable you don't always eat the whole plant. For example, when you eat peas you are eating the seeds of the pea plant.

 Look the lists below. In your book match up the vegetable to the part of the plant we eat.

• potato	• Roots
• beans, peas, sweet corn	• Tubers
• cabbage, lettuce, spinach, watercress	• Bulbs
• cucumber, egg plant, marrow, tomato	• Stems
• onions	• Leaves
• beetroot, carrots, parsnips, radishes	• Flowers
• asparagus, celery	• Seeds
• artichoke, broccoli, cauliflower	• Fruit

UNIT 4

Sprouting beans

It's very easy to grow your own vegetables. Here's one vegetable you can grow in your classroom.

TO SPROUT BEANS:

You need

- 1/4 cup beans - these can be mung or soya

Equipment

- one screw top jar with holes in the lid

Method

1. Wash the beans and soak overnight in cold water in the jar.

2. The next day drain off the water from the jar and put the jar in a warm place.

3. Rinse and drain the jar about three times a day.

   The bean sprouts should be ready to eat in about five days.

Bean sprouts can be used as a garnish and in salads, sandwiches, stir fries and chow mein.

Lots of seeds can also be sprouted on damp cotton wool or kitchen paper. Small seeds such as cress sprout very easily and quickly. You may like to try some of these.

- What could happen if you alter the way of sprouting beans suggested here? Find out by changing the conditions. Write a paragraph in your book about what you observed.

UNIT 4

Vegetable investigation

1. You probably know you need to eat vegetables, but do you know why? Ask three older people whom you know what their opinions are. Then do some library research on why vegetables are important. Write up your conclusion in a paragraph which begins, **"Vegetables are important because ..."**

2. Current research tells us that adults and young people are not eating enough fresh fruits and vegetables. As a class discuss how you can find out if this is true - then follow your investigation through.

3. Under the heading 'Vegie Table' keep a record of the vegetables you eat each day, for a week.

4. On a visit to your local supermarket find out about:

- vacuum packing
- chilling
- what 'hydroponics' means
- refrigeration

5. Use the results of your record to complete a class survey to find out what vegetables are eaten and how many servings are eaten on average each day.

6. Graph the results and use the information to say:

- whether or not your class is having, on average, five servings a day and is eating a variety of different vegetables;

- what vegetables on the list would not have been available without technological developments like the ones you found out about at the supermarket.

7. Write a poem, a rap, a limerick or a jingle encouraging people of your own age to eat more vegetables. You can set it to music if you like.

Milk - Getting the Good Guys Going

Why do we need milk?

People who do not have enough calcium in their diet are at risk, when they get older, of low bone density and possibly osteoporosis. As you get older bone density is gradually reduced. This means that bones will fracture easily, particularly the wrist, hip and spine. As you grow, it is important that you include enough calcium in your diet to build strong bones and to increase bone density. Milk (and milk products) is one of the best and most easily obtained sources of calcium. Other good sources include canned sardines, canned salmon, broccoli, silver beet, baked beans, oranges, peanuts, dried apricots and sesame seeds.

It is recommended that boys have 1200 mg of calcium daily and that girls have 1000 mg of calcium daily. The calcium should come from low fat dairy products, as an increase in fat intake is not desirable.

 Look at the calcium content of these dairy products. Then do the activity on the following page

DAIRY PRODUCT	SERVING	CALCIUM CONTENT
● milk	1 cup	390 mg
● cheese	25 g	145 mg
● yoghurt	150 ml	150 ml
● ice cream	2 scoops	135 mg
● milkshake	1 glass	180 mg

UNIT 5

Milk - Getting the Good Guys Going
How do you measure up?

Choose three people and ask them to monitor their intake of dairy products for one day.

● Show your class average for each of the milk products. Work out if the average meets the daily requirements for calcium for people of your age. Compare your own result with the class average. How did you measure up? Collate your results on a bar graph.

Milk Product	Serving Size	Person One Calcium Intake	Person Two Calcium Intake	Person Three Calcium Intake
Milk				
Cheese				
Yoghurt				
Ice cream				
Milk shake				

● How could you encourage yourself and your classmates to include enough milk in your daily diet?

UNIT 5

Milk - Getting the Good Guys Going

Task

Yoghurt is a quick healthy snack and is an easy way to encourage people to include more milk in their daily eating.

In this activity you will develop a flavoured yoghurt that people of your age will enjoy and eat often.

The great yoghurt taste

You've seen the adverts, you've heard the slogans, you may have even eaten a pot or two of yoghurt yourself. But how much do you really know about all those different sorts of yoghurt on the supermarket shelves?

High Fat　　**Frozen**

Full Fruit　　*Acidophilus*

Lite　　**LOW FAT**

Here's your chance to find out and compare them. Read about yoghurt tasting first.

So you want to be a yoghurt taster?

Does the thought of being paid to taste yoghurt appeal to you?

Milk - Getting the Good Guys Going

Rate the qualities of different yoghurts on the market

Now you know more about what taste testers do, see if you can set up a panel of your own.

- Set up a tasting panel in the classroom. Each student will need to have their own plate, saucer or plastic pottle and a spoon or wooden spatula.

- Your teacher will have organised for you a range of yoghurts in large pots with a variety of flavours, brands, high/low fat, fruit and plain.

- Help yourself to a small quantity using a serving spoon.

- Taste one yoghurt at a time and record your results before moving on.

Sample	taste	colour	texture	smell
1				
2				
3				
4				

- You may decide to have more than four samples to taste. Enlarge the chart if you do.

- Rate each sample 1 to 5 on a chart like the example above, with 5 being the best.

- Analyse class results, using a bar graph, to determine the most popular yoghurt.

Milk - Getting the Good Guys Going
Micro-organisms: good and bad guys

S mall organisms that can only be seen with a microscope are called *micro-organisms*. These are in the air around, on our skin and on work surfaces and equipment. They only grow and multiply when three essential conditions are present. These are:

● food

● warmth

● moisture

You might be more familiar with micro-organisms than you think. For example, have you ever left the milk out on the kitchen bench and found it 'off'?

This doesn't happen if you leave it in the fridge because cold temperatures (4°C) usually stop the bacteria from multiplying rapidly. You only need to take away *one* of the conditions necessary for growth to discourage micro-organisms like bacteria from multiplying; for example, dried fruit has the water removed, frozen pies are kept at a low temperature and bottled fruit is sterilised and sealed.

Some micro-organisms are useful to us, for example, special bacteria are used in yoghurt and cheese making. Yeast is used for making bread and ginger beer; and mould is used in blue vein cheese.

Milk - Getting the Good Guys Going
Making yoghurt

Y oghurt is a fermented milk product with a tangy taste and a smooth texture. It can be made from fresh or powdered milk.

You will be developing this recipe to make your own flavoured yoghurt. Although you will be encouraging yoghurt bacteria to grow you must make sure that these are the **only** bacteria growing! All utensils must be spotlessly clean and your hands must be washed before starting.

 Here is a basic yoghurt recipe for you to follow. Natural yoghurt is used as a starter as it contains the bacteria used for yoghurt making. These are alive and will grow and multiply in the right conditions.

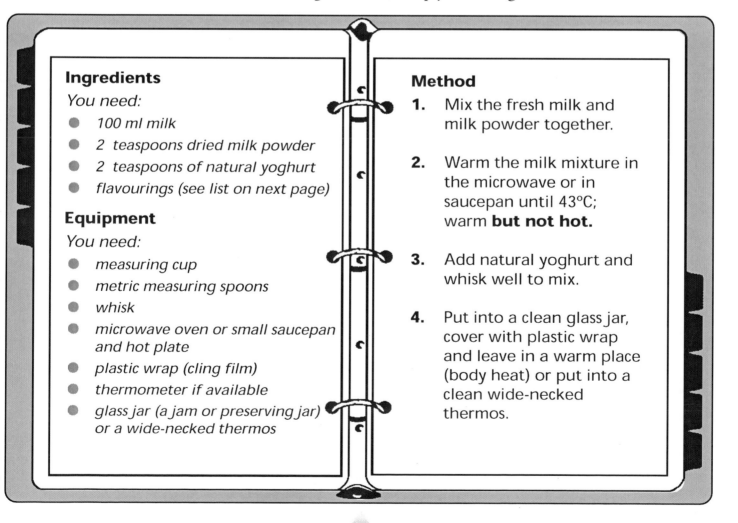

Ingredients
You need:
- *100 ml milk*
- *2 teaspoons dried milk powder*
- *2 teaspoons of natural yoghurt*
- *flavourings (see list on next page)*

Equipment
You need:
- *measuring cup*
- *metric measuring spoons*
- *whisk*
- *microwave oven or small saucepan and hot plate*
- *plastic wrap (cling film)*
- *thermometer if available*
- *glass jar (a jam or preserving jar) or a wide-necked thermos*

Method
1. Mix the fresh milk and milk powder together.

2. Warm the milk mixture in the microwave or in saucepan until 43°C; warm **but not hot.**

3. Add natural yoghurt and whisk well to mix.

4. Put into a clean glass jar, cover with plastic wrap and leave in a warm place (body heat) or put into a clean wide-necked thermos.

Milk - Getting the Good Guys Going
Making yoghurt

5. Leave for 4 - 6 hours.

6. Add a flavouring. Choose a flavouring or a way of serving yoghurt you will enjoy.

7. Chill. If the yoghurt is not cooled **immediately** after making the bacteria then they will continue to act and make the yoghurt very sour.

Suggested flavourings you might like to choose from:

- *berries*
- *stewed fruit*
- *dried fruits*
- *concentrated blackcurrant drink*
- *nuts*
- *powdered drink flavouring*
- *muesli*
- *raw fruit such as kiwi fruit*
- *pineapple*
- *mango*
- *strawberries*

Other ways of using yoghurt

- Plain yoghurt can be used instead of cream with fruit pies, steamed pudding or fruit salad.

- Yoghurt goes well with curries and Indian vegetable dishes, and Middle Eastern dishes such as lentils and eggplant.

- Yoghurt can be stirred into hot vegetable soups.

- Salads can be dressed with yoghurt dressing.

- Try a yoghurt smoothie as an alternative to a fizzy drink or cordial!

Milk - Getting the Good Guys Going
Some more recipes to try

YOGHURT ICE CREAM

Ingredients

You need:

- 2 cups plain yoghurt
- $1/2$ cup caster sugar
- $1/2$ teaspoon vanilla essence

Method:

1. Beat yoghurt with sugar and vanilla.

2. Pour the mixture into a shallow ice cream tray. Cover with foil and put in the freezer.

3. When it is about half frozen take it out of the freezer and either put into a food processor or whisk thoroughly until smooth.

4. Return to the freezer until solid.

5. Soften in the refrigerator for about 30 minutes, then serve with fresh orcooked fruit.

FRUIT SMOOTHIE

Method:

1. Cook and cool some unsweetened fruit such as raspberries, strawberries or apples.

2. Place in a food processor 2 tablespoons of fruit slices. Blend lightly.

3. Add 2 teaspoons of runny honey, $3/4$ cup of plain unsweetened yoghurt and $1/4$ cup of milk.

4. Process until smooth. Do not overprocess.

Other fruits make good smoothies too. You might like to try some.

Evaluate your product

- Have a class taste testing like the one you had with the bought yoghurts.

- Make your own score chart or use the one in the first taste testing, to rate the yoghurts and to choose the most popular one.

Don't Get Browned Off!

PREPARATION

Access to a computer for data analysis and presentation would be an advantage in this unit of work. The Internet could be used for reporting.

Some discussions of what enzymes are is important before work begins.

Students need to deal with boiling water in this activity. Ensure that this part is properly supervised.

ABOUT ENZYMES

Enzymes are chemicals found in both plant and animal cells. In fruit and vegetables they speed up reactions, leading to ripening and softening as well as changes in colour, texture and flavour.

In the body enzymes aid many processes such as digestion and energy production.

Enzymes are more active in warm, moist conditions. Activity slows down at lower temperatures. This is why cool stores are often used to keep fruit and vegetables fresher, and why they go 'off' in warm conditions. Enzymes are destroyed at temperatures above 70°C. Enzymes are also inactive when moisture is removed, such as in dehydration.

Don't Get Browned Off!

Enzymes in the mouth

 To find out how enzymes work in your mouth, try this.

- Chew a piece of bread for about two minutes without swallowing.

- Did you note any changes in taste? Describe to another person how it tasted.

- If your bread became sweeter, this change is caused by an enzyme in saliva called amylase, which begins starch digestion in the mouth. Other enzymes in the intestines complete the digestion of starch so that it can be absorbed and used by the body for energy.

Why does your apple core go brown?

 One of the changes caused by enzymes is the browning of some fruit and vegetables when they are cut. Work in groups to find out how this can be prevented. Discuss too why this prevention might be valuable to producers, marketers and consumers.

You will need:

- an apple (try several varieties)
- lemon juice
- sugar
- vinegar
- salt
- boiling water
- a plate
- chopping board
- vegetable knife
- measuring jug
- teaspoon
- six small bowls or jam jars
- scraps of paper for labels
- refrigerator

Don't Get Browned Off!

Why does your apple core go brown?

What to do:

1. Label the six bowls or jam jars as follows:

    - Salt
    - Sugar
    - Lemon Juice
    - Hot Water
    - Vinegar
    - Cold Water

2. Prepare the same labels for the plate and two others saying 'Untreated' and 'Cold'.

3. Put 200 ml of cold water into five of the bowls and 200 ml of boiling water into the sixth one. **Take care with the boiling water!**

4. Add one teaspoon of salt, sugar, vinegar to the appropriate bowl or jar. Stir to mix.

5. Cut the apple into slices (at least seven) and put one slice into each of the bowls or jars, one slice in the refrigerator and one on the plate by the 'Untreated' label.

6. Take the slices out of the bowls or jars and carefully place beside the correct label on the plate. Leave to stand untouched.

7. Observe what happens to the slices after five minutes, ten minutes twenty minutes and thirty minutes.

8. Draw up a chart like the one on the next page to record your results.

9. After 30 minutes, and when you have recorded all of your other results, taste the apple slices and write down words to describe the colour, flavour, and texture of them.

Don't Get Browned Off!

Why does your apple core go brown?

Time	Treatment	Colour	Texture	Flavour
5 minutes				
10 minutes				
20 minutes				
30 minutes				

10. Write down which method you think is the best one to stop apples browning without affecting the flavour and texture.

11. Discuss your results with the class. Was there a difference between apple varieties?

12. Remember to wash and tidy up!

Don't Get Browned Off!
Make your own fruit snack

Task

Use the information you have about how to prevent fruit browning and make a fruit snack. This could be for the class, for sale to other classes or to sell in the school canteen.

- Think about all the possibilities for fruit snacks and discuss as a class which are the most suitable. You will need to consider your facilities, food hygiene, and what low cost or seasonal fruits are available.

- Use the method you have found most effective to prevent fruits from browning.

- Decide as a class whether to make fresh fruit or dehydrated fruit snacks. You might like to experiment with fruit leather as well. A commercial dehydrator is recommended for large quantities of dehydrated fruits.

- When you have decided on a fresh or dehydrated fruit snack you are ready to start planning.

PLANNING

1. Survey your target group to find out preferences for fruits to use.

2. Investigate ideas for fruit snacks and trial a range.

3. Research sources and costs of raw fruit.

4. Prepare an advertising campaign to promote the fruit snack you have developed.

5. Plan a time line for the purchase, preparation and selling or serving of the snack.

6. List tasks and assign responsibilities.

Don't Get Browned Off!
Batch production

 When you have a lot of product to make you need to use the **batch production** method. This a way of making lots of the same product quickly and efficiently. You will need to:

1. Calculate the quantities of fruit to buy (you may wish to take pre-orders to avoid wastage)

2. Identify the processes involved in the production.

   These could include:

   - preparing the work surfaces

   - washing the fruit

   - treating the fruit to prevent browning

   - assembling or dehydrating the chosen product

   - wrapping, presenting and labelling the snack

   - storing of the snack before use

   - distributing to the target group

3. Evaluate the products and the process you used to make the snack.

   You will need to consider:

   - quality of the finished product

   - customer satisfaction

   - efficiency of the production line

   - wastage and hygiene

   - cost effectiveness

4. Write a one page report about this project to inspire other classes to try something similar. You might even put your report onto the Internet!

Healthy Habits Award

is hereby presented to

....

For eating healthily and exercising well for a period of one week

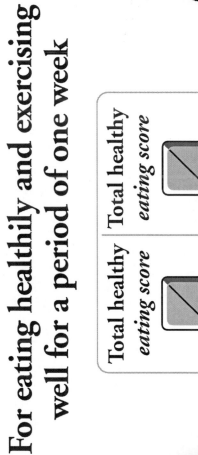

Total healthy eating score	Total healthy eating score
⬜	⬜

Date:..............

Parent signature:..............   Teacher signature:..............